FiRST WORDS
STiCKER ACTiViTiES

At Home

This is a house. It has windows and a door. Can you color it in?

Help set the table! Find a plate, knife, and fork on the sticker pages.

Can you find five teddy bears hidden in the bedroom? Now color it in!

table

lamp

chair

bed

Now fill this house with drawings of the things you would like in it!

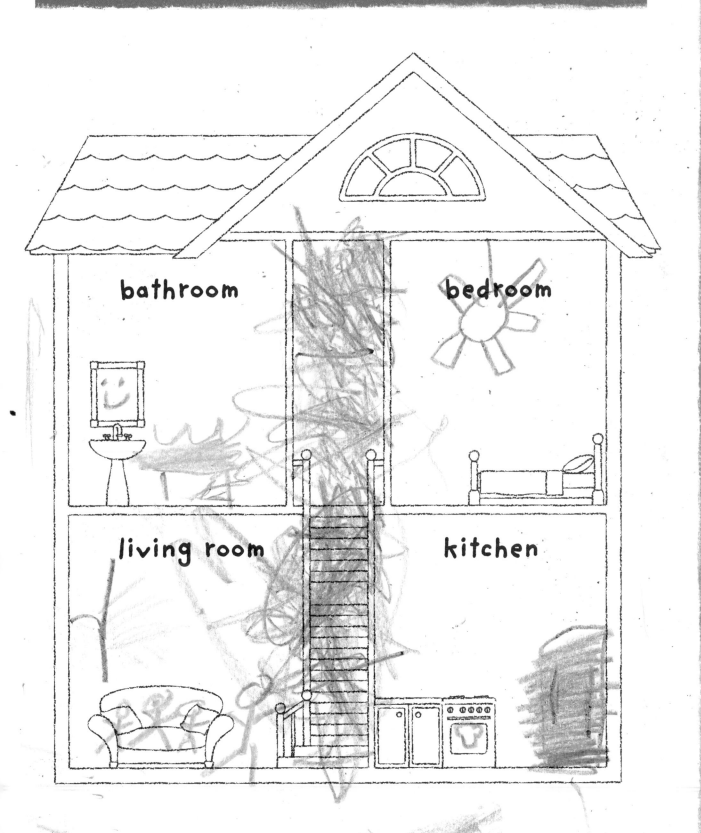

bathroom

bedroom

living room

kitchen

In the Yard

Some houses have yards outside
with trees, grass, and flowers. Find
some flowers on the sticker pages to
add to the flowerpots.

Can you find some bird stickers
to put near the birdfeeder?

Out and About

At preschool

At preschool, children can play and learn!
Trace the lines on the blackboard.

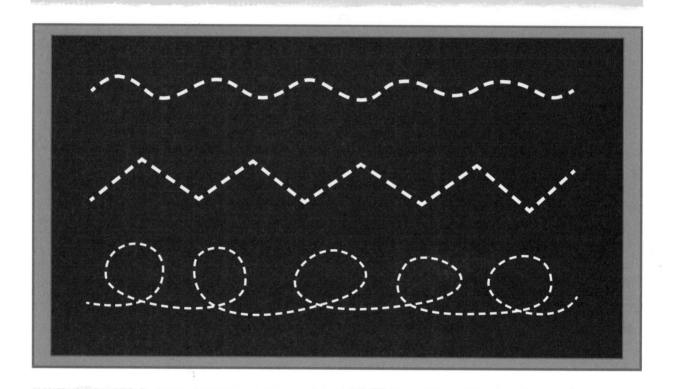

Can you find each of these
jars of paint on the sticker pages?

Count how many of each object you can see, then write the answer!

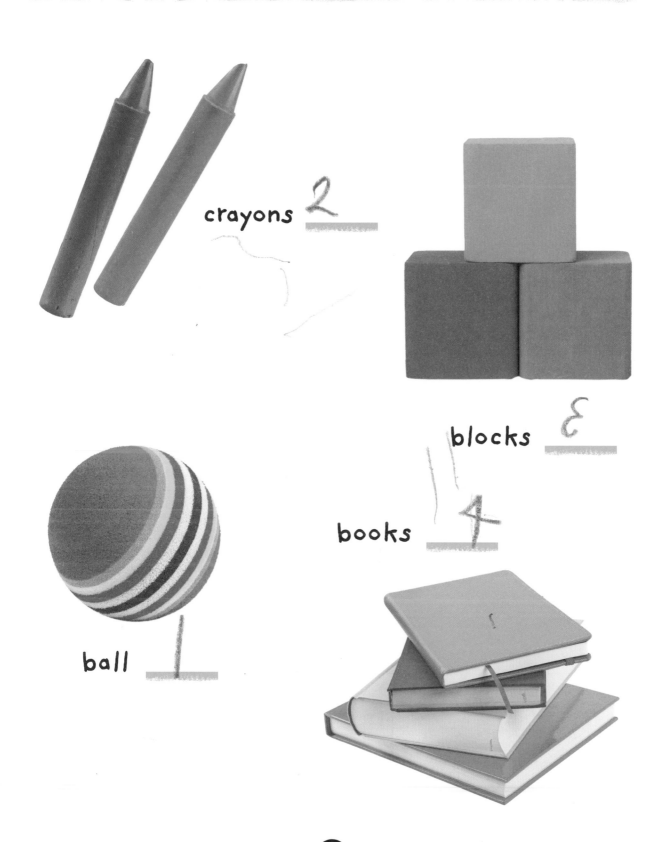

crayons 2

blocks 3

books 4

ball 1

Shops and other places

At the grocery store, you can buy fruit and vegetables. Find some fruit and vegetable stickers and add them to the basket.

At the library, you can borrow books to read. Can you draw and color a picture on this book's cover?

At the bakery, you can buy bread and cakes. Can you find stickers for these things the baker needs?

eggs

apron

mixing bowl and whisk

scale

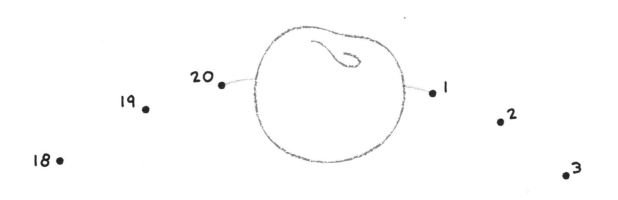

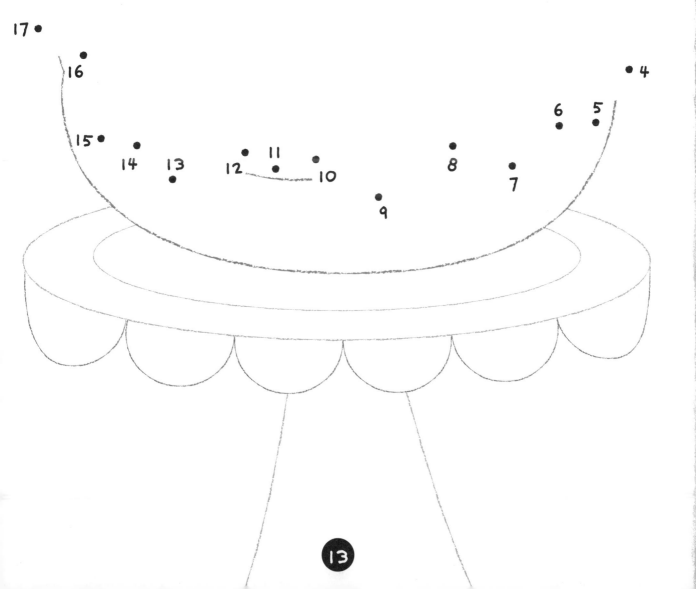

Things That Go

There are many different
things that go.
Can you find the stickers for these
things that go on the road?

Color in the tricycle, then decorate it with stickers!

A tricycle is like a bicycle, but it has three wheels.

Many things travel on the water. Can you finish the drawing of the boat?

Draw lines to connect the matching boats.

ship

rowboat

canoe

canoe

rowboat

ship

You are at the train station! Can you write your name on the train ticket?

Find a train sticker to put on tracks!

If you are traveling to another country, you need a passport. Draw a picture of yourself in this passport.

How many airplanes are flying through the sky?

Food

Breakfast time!
Breakfast is the first meal of the day. Can you find these breakfast foods on the sticker pages?

milk

yogurt

juice

egg

cereal

What is your favorite thing to eat for breakfast? Can you draw it on the plate?

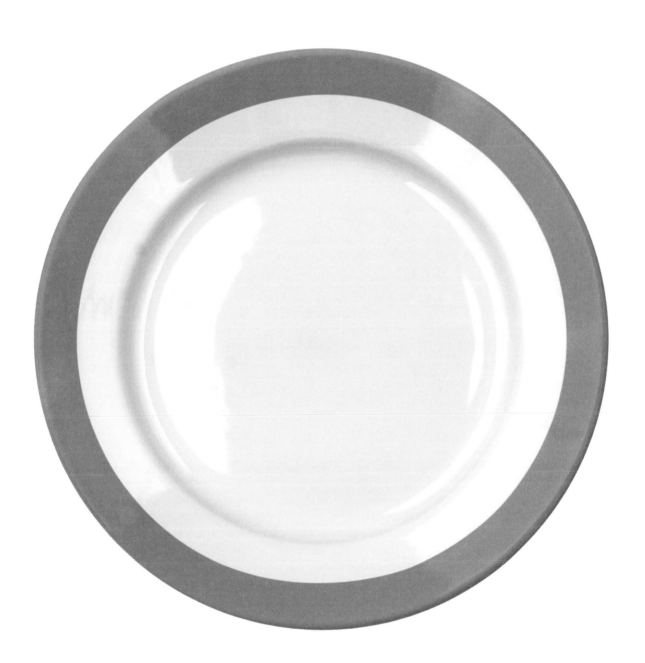

Lunch time!

Lunch is eaten in the middle of the day. Can you fill this yummy sandwich using the stickers?

Color in the pictures of fruit!

apple

pear

banana

cherries

strawberry

Snack time!

We often eat a snack in the afternoon to give us energy. Count the chocolate chips on each cookie and write the number on the line.

Draw some funny faces on these vegetables!

Dinnertime!

Dinner is the meal we eat in the evening. Find the stickers for the dinner plate face below, then draw the missing features.

Can you lead Emma through the maze to the dinner table?

Pets

Pets are animals that live with you at home.

A pet rabbit lives in a hutch. Can you find some **rabbit stickers** to add to the hutch?

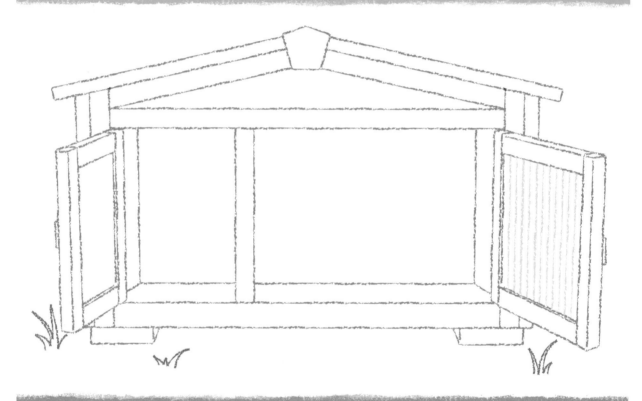

Can you trace the word "cat"?

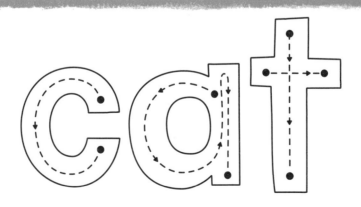

Can you find four differences between these two cat pictures?

Dogs like to chase balls. Follow the lines to find out which ball belongs to which dog!

29

Farm Animals

Some animals live on farms.

Cows give us milk.

A baby cow is called a calf.

Color in this cow and her calf.

A sheep's fluffy coat is called a fleece. We use fleece to make wool for clothing. Can you finish the drawing of the sheep and lambs?

A lamb is a baby sheep.

Chickens lay the eggs that we eat for breakfast. How many eggs can you find hidden in this scene?

Ocean Animals

Some animals live in water.
Add some brightly-colored fish stickers
to the coral reef.

How many dolphins do you see?

Color in these sea stars.

Savannah Animals

Some animals live in the savannah,
where it is hot and dry.

Elephants flap their big ears
to keep cool.

Trace the elephant's ears and trunk!

Can you find the giraffe's babies on the sticker pages?

Woodland Animals

Some animals live in the forests and woods, where there are a lot of trees.

Color in this family of foxes!

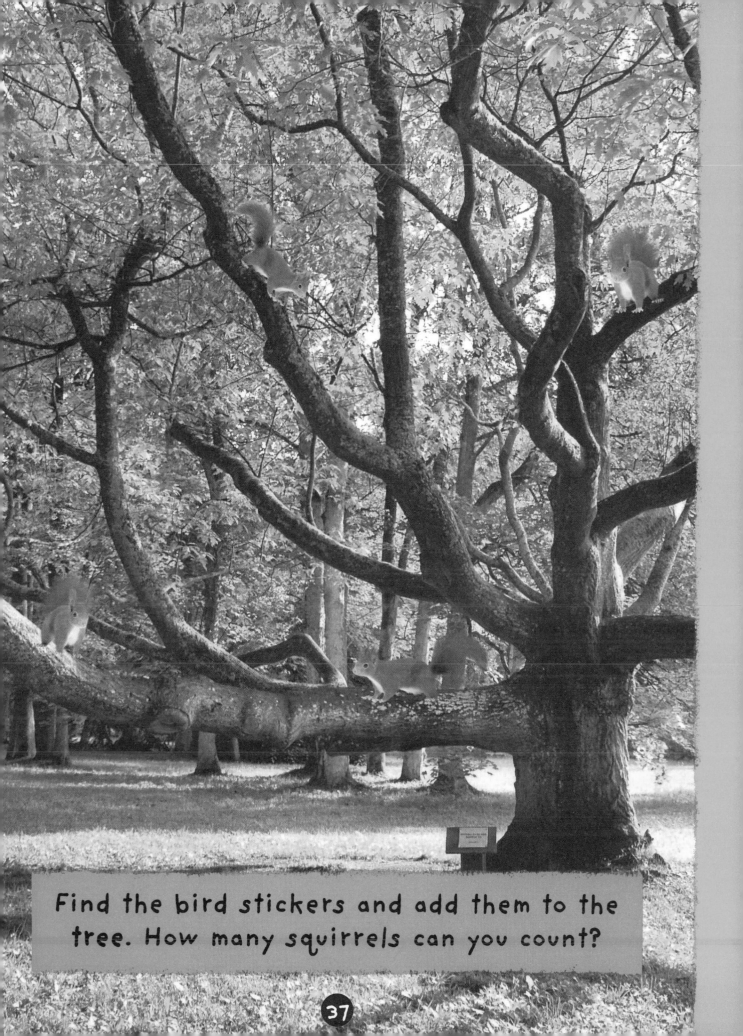

Find the bird stickers and add them to the tree. How many squirrels can you count?

Insects and Bugs

Insects and bugs are small creatures.
Some have wings and some
have lots of legs!

Find stickers for these insects and
add them to this scene!

Can you complete the spider's web, and then draw a friendly spider?

Seasons

Spring

Many animals have babies in the spring. Add some lamb stickers to this meadow scene!

Spring is the season when flowers appear and trees grow green leaves.

Can you color in the flowers in this garden?

Summary

Summer is the season when the sun shines and the weather can be hot.

beach umbrella

beach ball

towel

seashell

Find the stickers for these items you would find at the beach.

pail and shovel

Color and decorate this T-shirt and pair of shorts!

Fall

Fall is the **season** when the leaves change color, then fall off the trees.

How many pumpkins can you see in the pumpkin patch?

Fall is when farmers harvest, or pick, some of their crops. Can you find the stickers for the crops below?

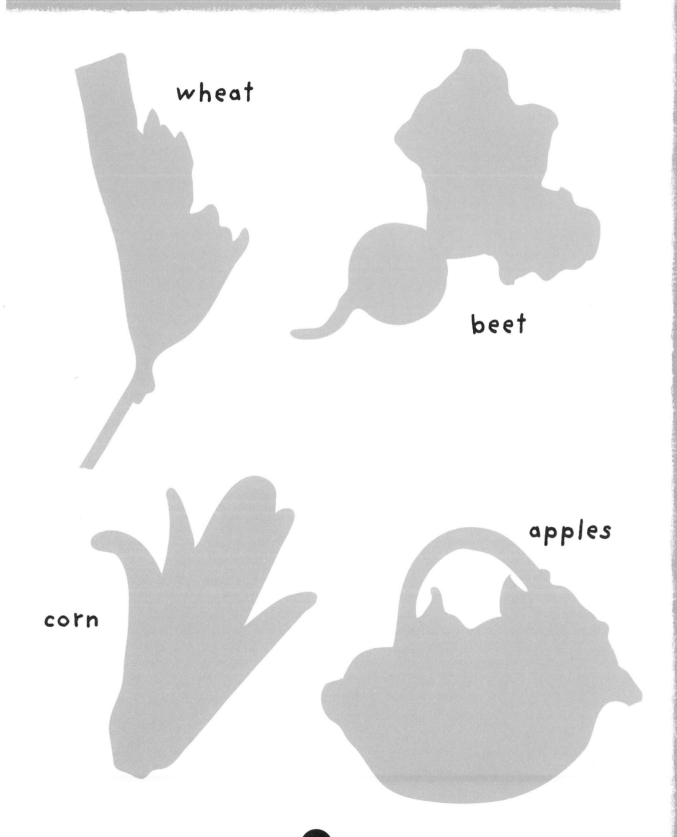

wheat

beet

apples

corn

Winter

Winter is the season when the weather can get very cold. Some places even get snow!

Color and decorate this snowman.

Complete the drawing of the snowflake!

Can you color and decorate this warm scarf?

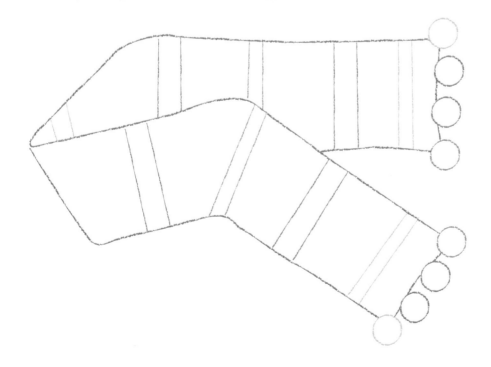

47

Color in the rain droplets and find the sticker of the umbrella.

Can you find the sticker for this pair of sunglasses? Then trace and color the sun!

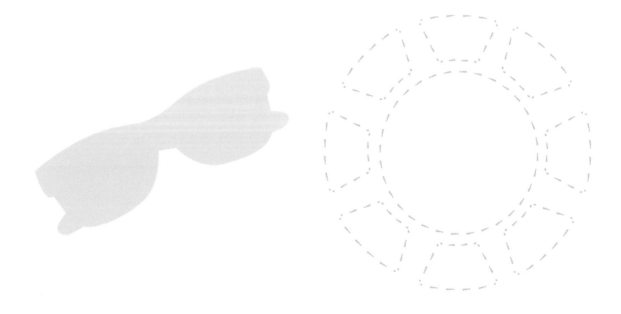

Wind makes pinwheels turn. Color and decorate this pinwheel.

People like to go skiing on mountains in the snow. Can you find the stickers for the ski items below?

Playtime

It's a lot of fun to play on the playground.

Can you draw yourself playing
on the seesaw?

Color in this fun merry-go-round!

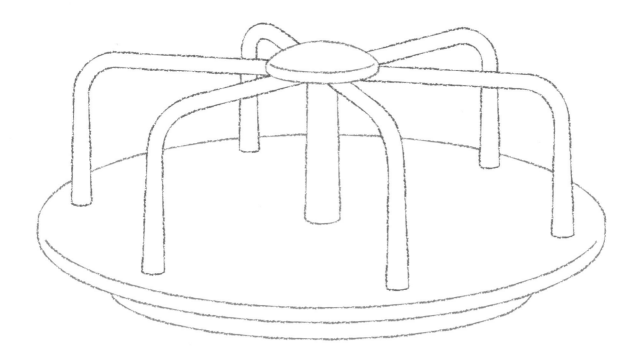

Connect the dots to see something else you would find at the playground.

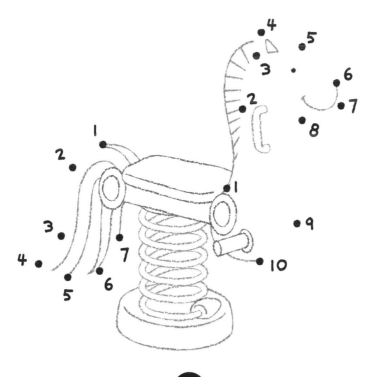

Can you find the stickers for these outdoor game items?

bowling

hoppity ball

tennis racket
and ball

Hula-Hoop

jump rope

Bella has lost her ball. Can you lead her through the maze to find it?

Trace the word "play."

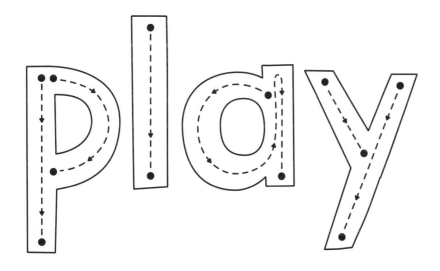

Toys

Follow the lines to find each child's favorite toy!

bear

blocks

puzzle

boat

Color in the toy train.

Can you find the robot that looks different from the others?

Use your stickers to complete this tower of blocks.

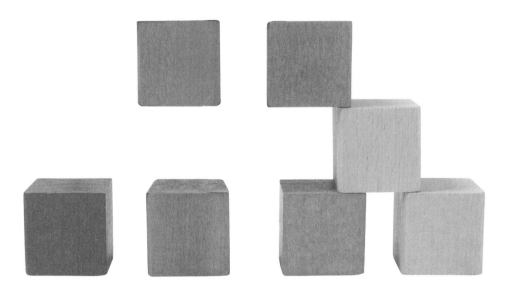

Color in the toy elephant!

Draw lines to match the toys.

Colors

Can you find the stickers for these red items?

apple

tomato

cherries

rose

What color are these items?

chick

hard hat

banana

How many blue balloons can you count?

Can you find the object that looks different from the others?

Can you color the tractor green?

60

Draw lines to match these purple items.

Now can you name all the colors on this paint palette?

g _ _ _ _

r _ _

y _ _ _ _ _

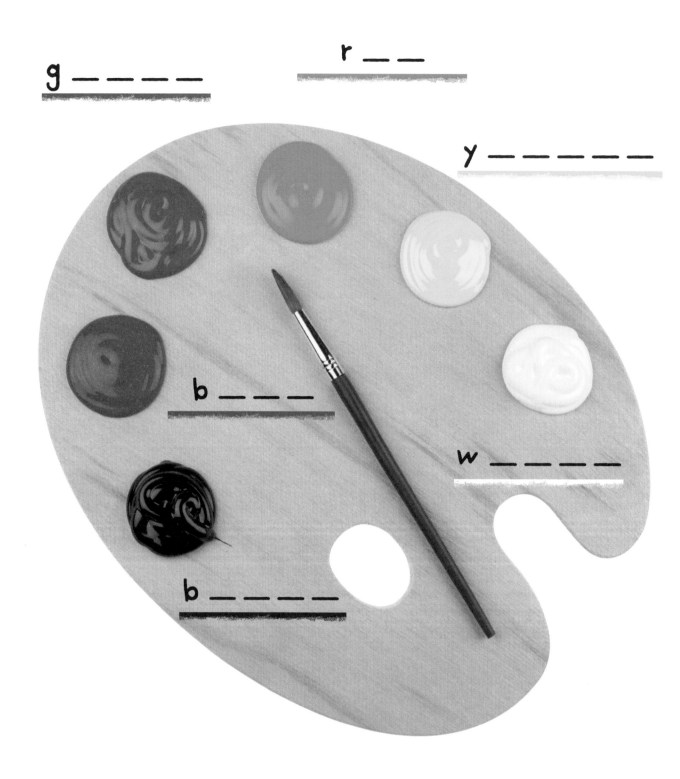

b _ _ _ _

w _ _ _ _ _

b _ _ _ _ _

Draw and color your own picture on this canvas.

Shapes

Can you color in the school?

 The roof of the school is a triangle.

 The windows of the school are **squares**.

 The doors of the school are **rectangles**.

 The wheels on the **bus** are circles.

Trace the wheels and decorate
the bus with stickers.

Actions

This puppy has been out for a walk. Color in his pawprints.

Can you find the stickers for these animals that hop?

rabbit

kangaroo

frog

grasshopper

Who can run the fastest? Follow the lines to see who won the race!

Can you color in the jump rope?

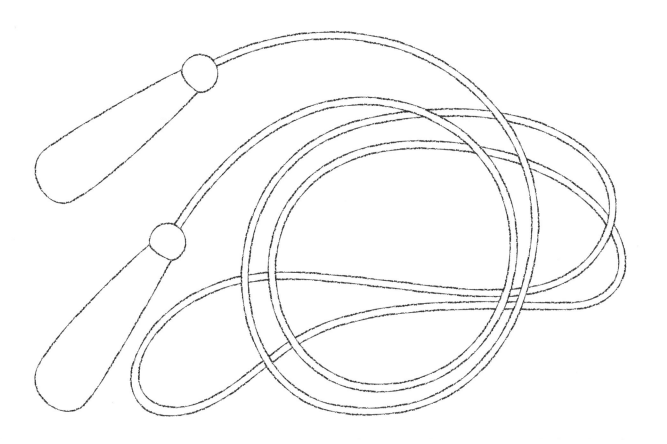

Trace the word "jump."

69

Draw arrows from the word to the body part.

head

arm

hand

foot

leg

Give this face some eyes, a nose, a mouth, and some ears!

Draw lines to match these items to the correct body parts.

sunglasses

gloves

hat

shoes

Now add arms, legs, and faces to these splotches to make funny characters!

The End of the Day

Can you find 5 rubber duck stickers to add to the tub? Now draw more bubbles!

Can you lead the rubber duck through the maze to find its friend?

Find the stickers for these bath time items.

soap

towel

bubble bath

It's time to get ready for bed!
Draw lines to match the items that
go together.

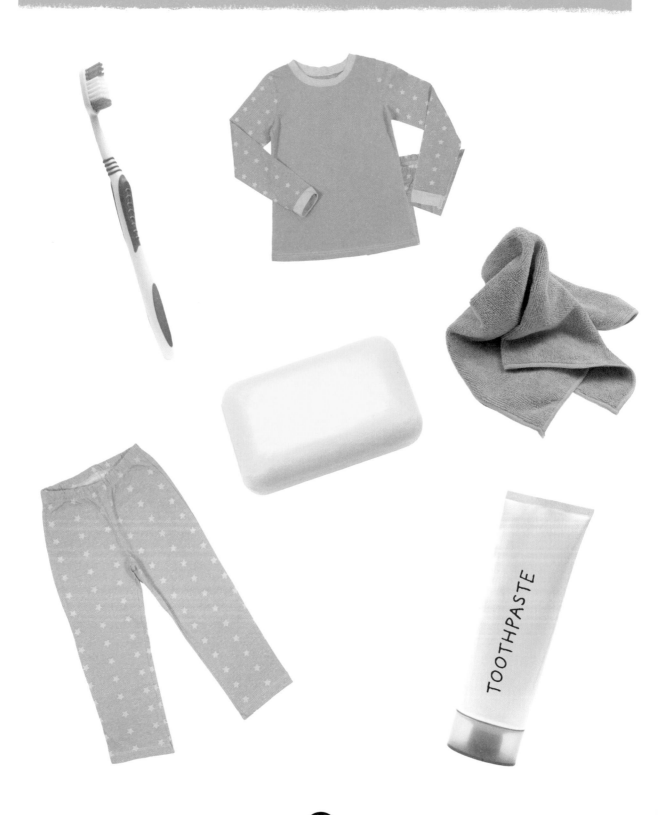

TOOTHPASTE

Good night, bear!

ANSWERS

Page 9:

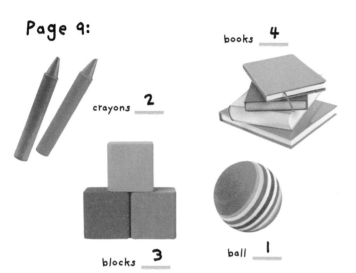

crayons **2**

books **4**

blocks **3**

ball **1**

Page 17:

Page 19: There are three airplanes in the sky.

Page 24:

2

4

3

5

1

Page 27:

Page 29:

Page 31: There are five eggs.

Page 32: There are two dolphins.

Page 37: There are four squirrels.

Page 44: There are five pumpkins.

ANSWERS

Page 53:

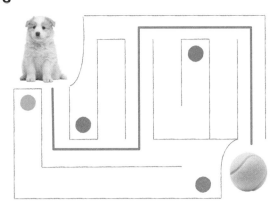

Page 54:

Page 55:

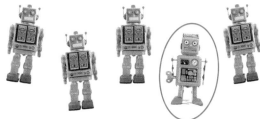

Page 57:

Page 59: There are four blue balloons.

Page 60:

Page 61:

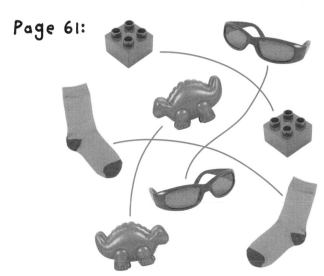

Page 62:

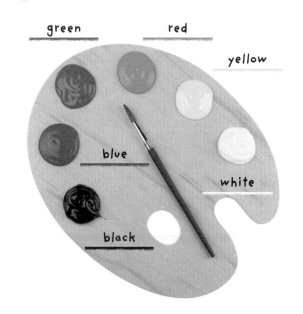

ANSWERS

Page 68:

Page 70:

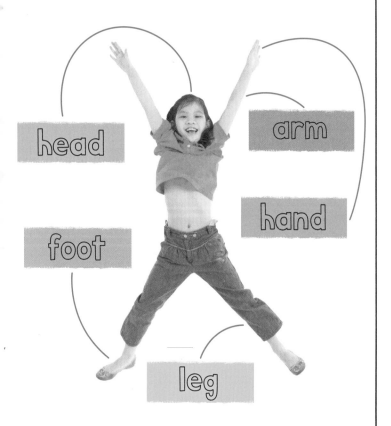

head

arm

foot

hand

leg

Page 72:

Page 75:

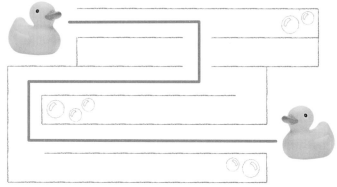

Page 76:

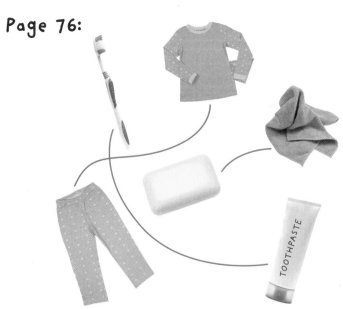

Orange

Blue

Purple

Green

Yellow

Red

butterfly

ladybug

beetle

caterpillar

bee

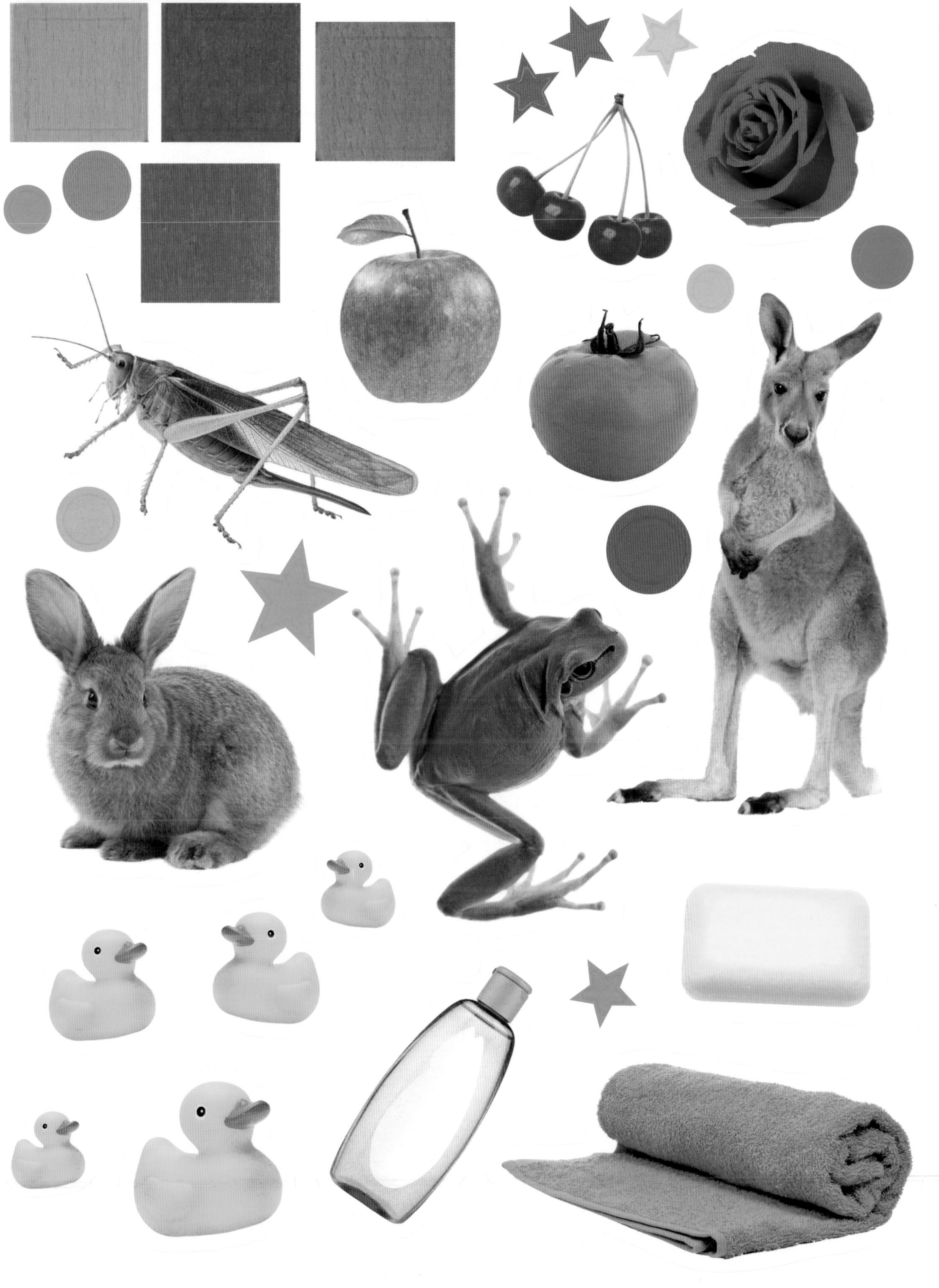

Things That Go

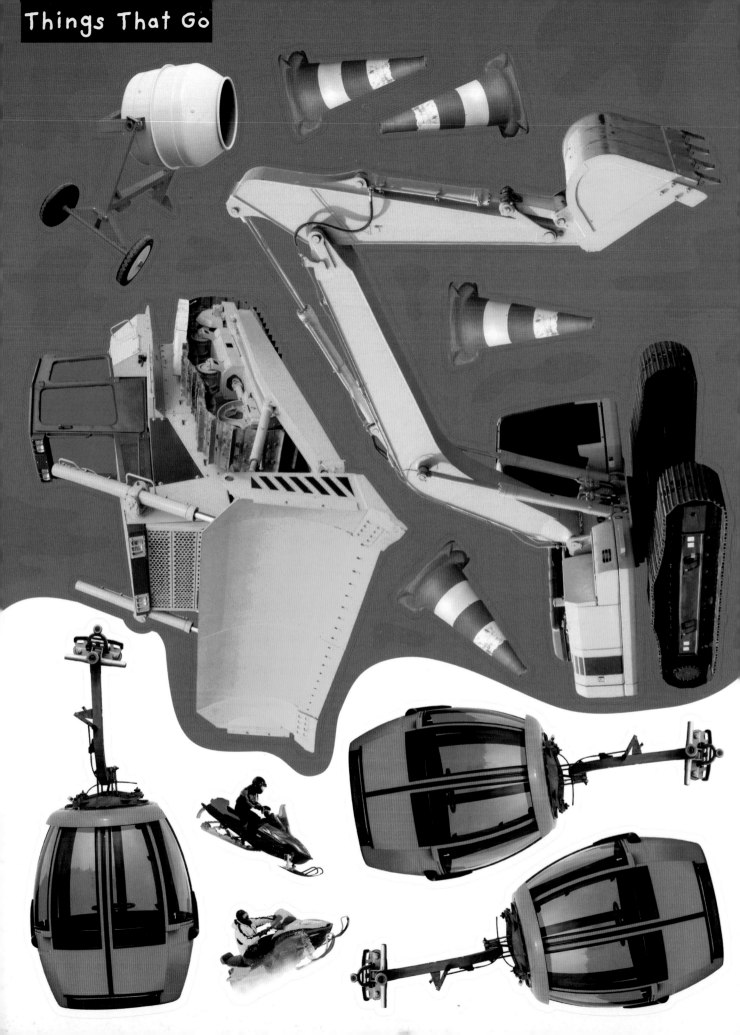

THiNGS THAT GO
STiCKER ACTiViTiES

These vehicles won't go anywhere without wheels! See if you can find some wheel stickers to add.

bicycle

truck

car

tractor

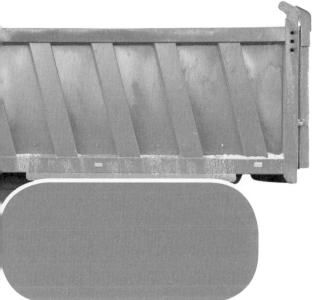

horse and cart

83

Put some speedy race cars on the track.

Color in this busy ocean scene.

86

How many boats can you see? How many submarines can you see?

Trace the dotted lines
to complete the picture
of the helicopter.

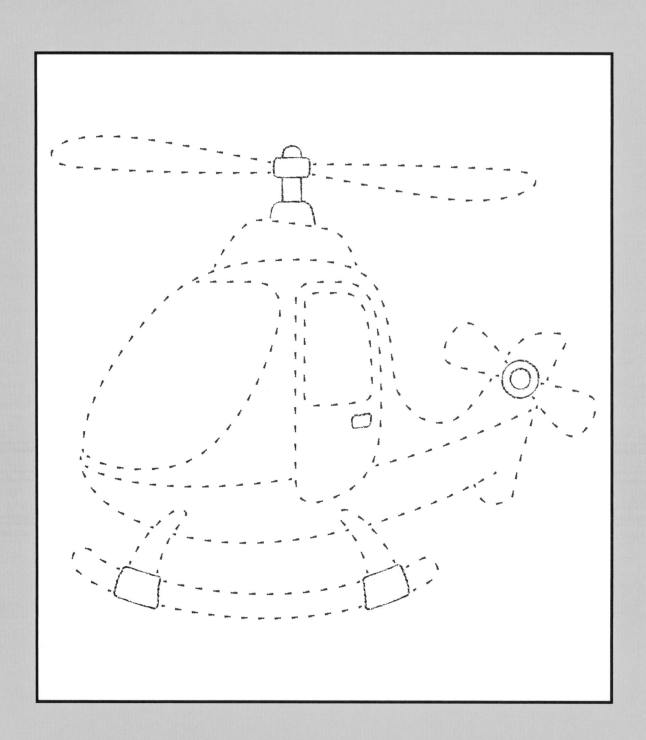

Can you color these in?

garbage truck

forklift

digger

school bus

90

rocks

heavy
boxes

children

garbage bags

What's this little car towing?

Now use your imagination to draw what this car is towing.

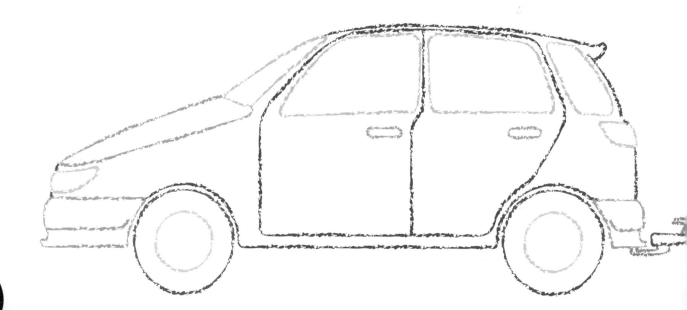

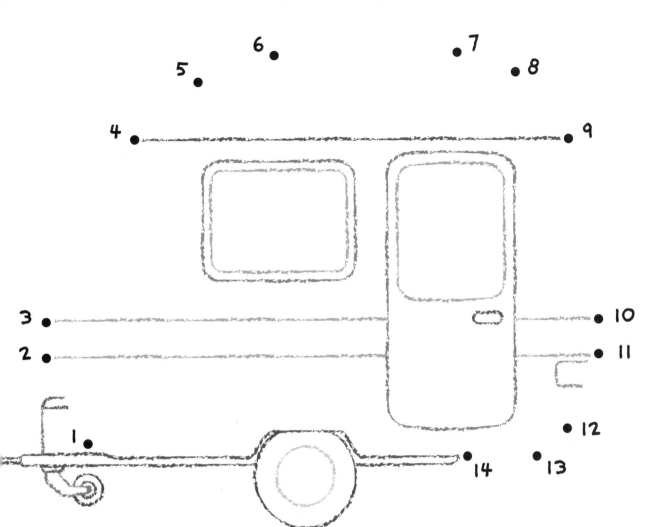

6

5

7

8

4

9

3

2

10

11

1

12

14

13

93

Which train is going to the station?

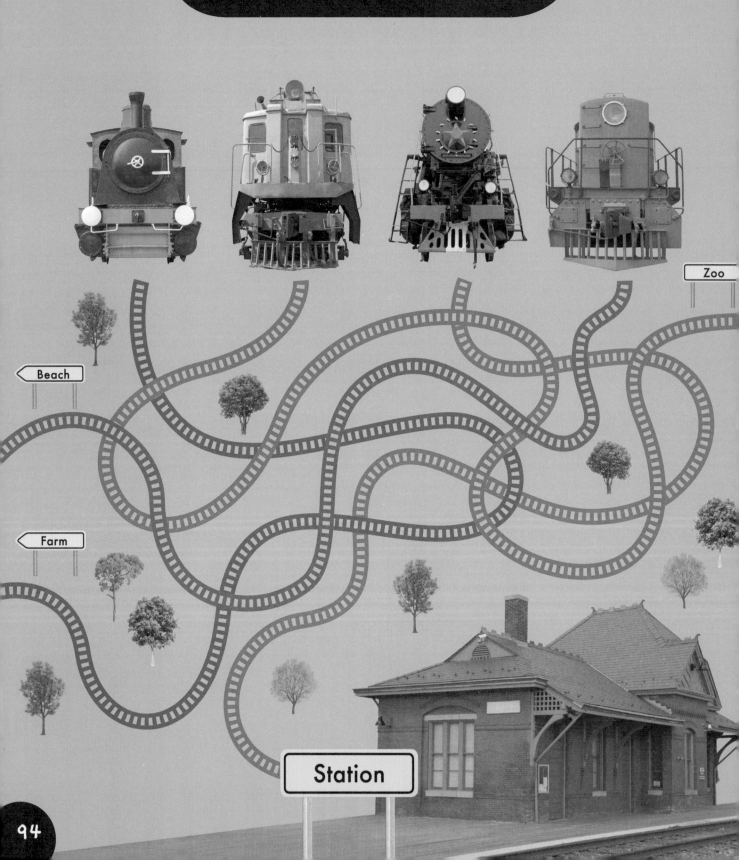

Zoo

Beach

Farm

Station

Color in this train and decorate it with stickers.

Add some sailboat
stickers to the lake.

Design your own road signs!

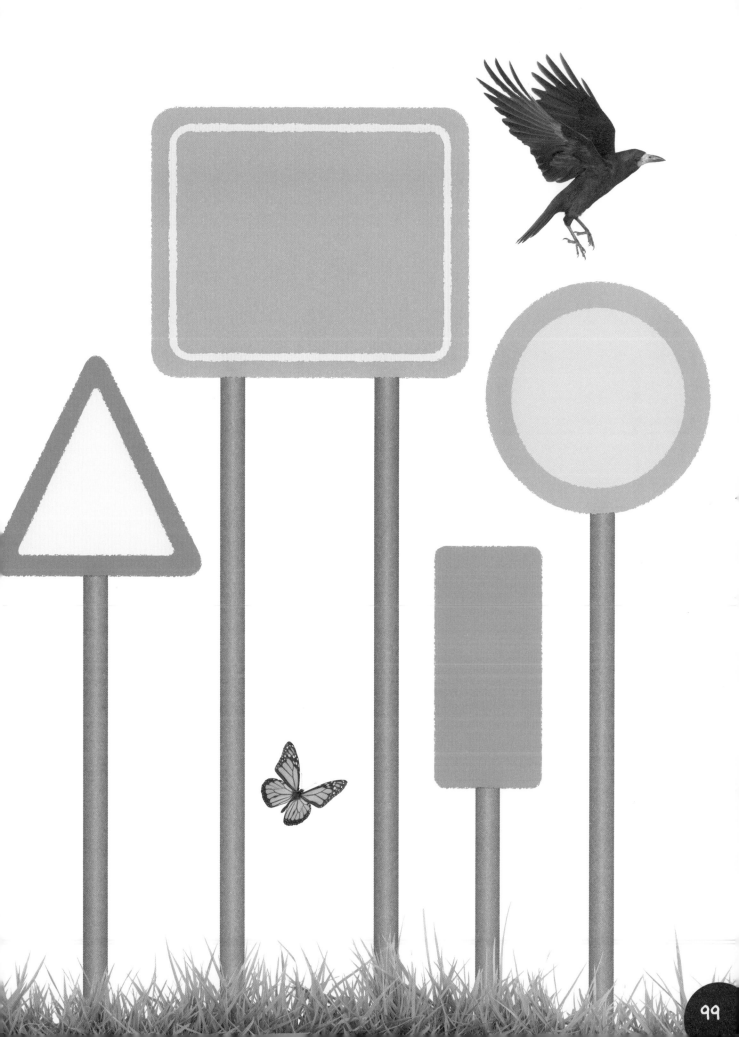

Look on the sticker pages
and find the stickers for
these things that go.

bi-plane

sailboat

kayak

train

Draw a space
shuttle for this
astronaut.

Monster trucks
can crush cars!
Color this one in
and decorate it.

Now design your own mighty machine.

This airport is looking empty! Add some planes and baggage trucks.

Help the police car find the robbers!

Draw your own
police car.

Add a space
shuttle sticker to
zoom to the moon.

Now add some astronaut and satellite stickers.

Fill the sky with hot air balloon stickers.

How many blue balloons can you count? How many red ones?

Connect the dots to see what's about to blast off.

Can you find 5 differences between these airplanes? Now color them in.

Before there were cars, people traveled by horse and buggy. Place the horse and buggy stickers in front of the museum.

117

What stickers can you find to add to this construction site?

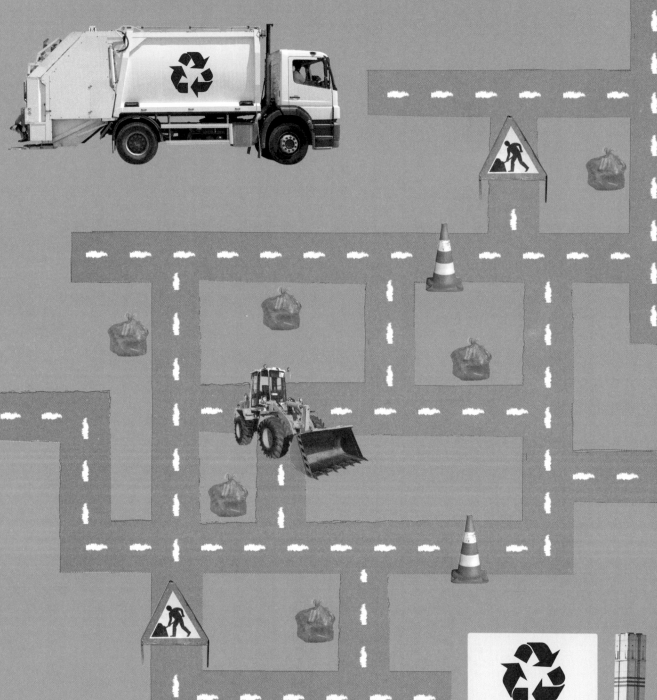

Help the truck pick up
all the bags and bring them
to the recycling center.

recycling center

Use crayons to color
these race cars.

Can you find a snowmobile to zoom down the mountain?

Hang some trams onto the cables.

123

Add some airplanes to the sky.

What doesn't belong in
the sea in this picture?
What doesn't
belong in the sky?

Use the grid to copy the sailboat.

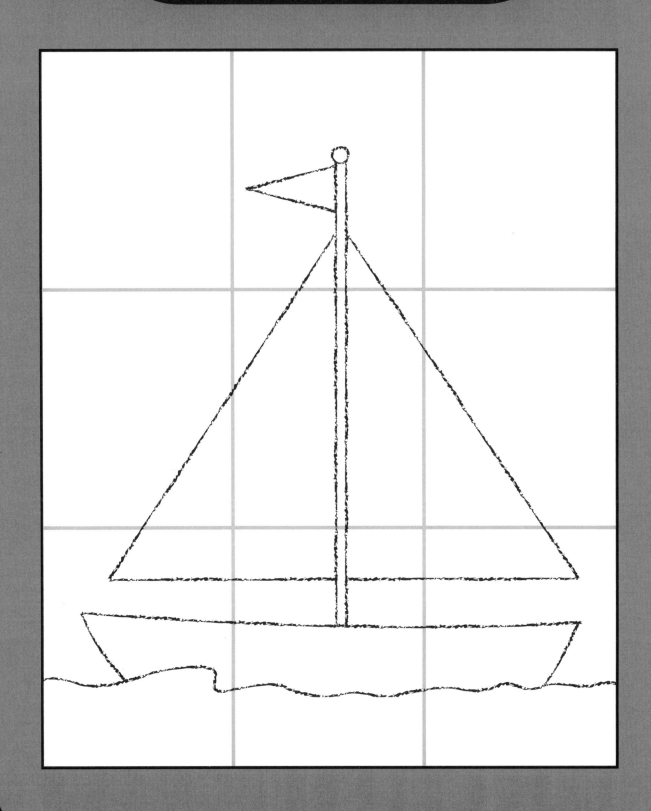

Now color it in.

What a lot of shiny tractors! Find the matching pairs and draw lines to connect them.

130

What things can you add to the land, water, and sky from the sticker pages?

Bumper cars are designed to crash into each other! Color in these crashing, smashing amusement park rides.

Some bridges open up to let tall boats pass through.

Use your stickers to add some boats to the river and some vehicles to the road.

Find the two trucks that are the same and circle them.

Can you find 5 differences in these pictures?

Helicopters land on helipads. Look for the "H" to see where to put the helicopter sticker.

What other stickers can you add to the scene?

Use your crayons and your imagination to turn these shapes into vehicles!

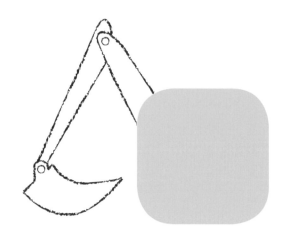

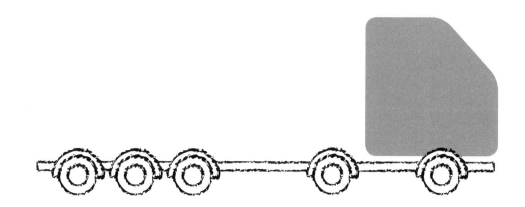

What a busy train station!
Color in the scene.

Add some construction
stickers to this scene.

Can you find some boats to float on the water?

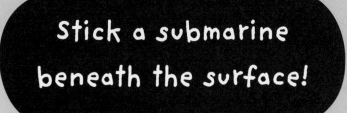

Stick a submarine beneath the surface!

Color in these things that go.

Which one do you like best, and why?

Can you find some snowmobile stickers to add to the mountains?

152

These huskies are trained to pull sleds. Find the sled sticker to add to the end of the reins.

A monorail is a train that runs on a single track high above the ground.

Can you add a train to the tracks on the ground and to the tunnel below?

Add some cars
to this parking
garage.

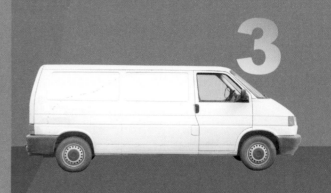

3

2

1

157

ANSWERS

Pages 86-87: There are 6 boats and 2 submarines.

Pages 90-91:

Pages 92-93: It's a camper!

Page 94:

Page 100

sailboat

train

kayak

bi-plane

Page 106:

Pages 110-111: There are 3 blue balloons and 5 red balloons.

Page 112:

It's a space shuttle!

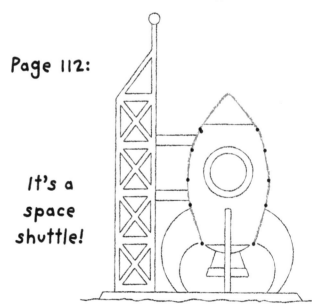

ANSWERS

Page 113:

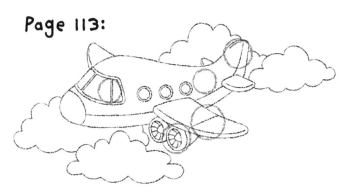

Page 120:

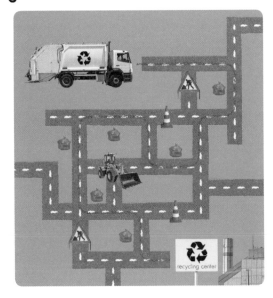

Pages 126-127: The ferry does not belong in the sky. The space shuttle does not belong in the sea.

Pages 130-131:

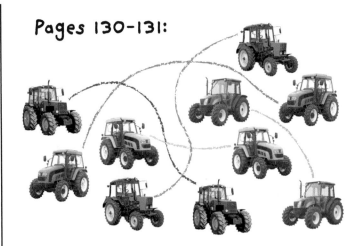

Page 138:

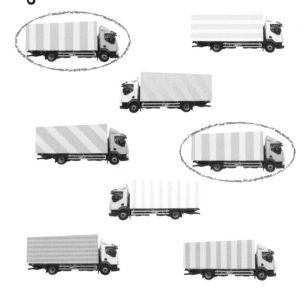

Page 139:

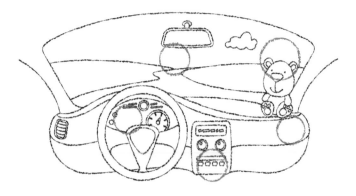

Good-bye, things that go!